Please return this item to any Poole library by the due date.
Renew on (01202) 265200 or at www.boroughofpoole.com/libraries

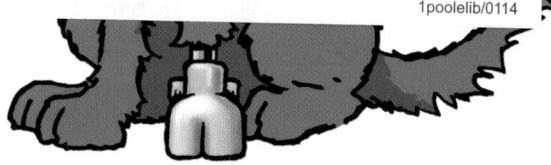

Written by Heather Chamberlain
Illustrated by Robin Edmonds

 For my Dad, Wally

CHAPTER IN VERSE

MONTY

The Major sorting through old clothes
(with mind still on those blasted crows)
then asked Marie, what 'kinder' way
would she propose to save the day?

She said, "To keep your crops from harm
without causing too much alarm,
don't shoot the crows to boost your yield,
stake out a scarecrow in the field."

The pair then set about the task
to build a scarecrow that would last
When almost done, the Major said,
"What shall we use to make his head?"

They 'Umm...d' and 'Ahh...d' for quite a while
for something that would suit its style
Marie said,"Don't use sack and string,
I think I might know just the thing."

And so she did. It worked a treat
and with some pulleys for its feet,
an army jacket, trousers too
they'd done the best that they could do.

"This is Monty," the Major said,
plonking a beret on his head
"A Field Marshall, I now propose
a title that befits his clothes."

Marie replied, "That sounds so grand."
He'd pride of place upon the land
until the night (or so it's said)
a bolt of lightning struck his head.

Electrified, he took a breath,
moved his right arm, then his left
His legs then wiggled, head could roll
and in a trice, slid off the pole.

As day then dawned, with life anew
(once he'd worked out what legs could do)
he soon sped off, at quite a speed
on tricky, whizzy feet, indeed!

He first found Happy Bottom's Barn
(had no intent to cause alarm)
but as he wheeled into the gloom
"Oh no!" squealed Panic, "we're all doomed!"

Scurry, Fireside, Woofbot, too
said, "Get a grip. What's up with you?"
Panic stuttered, "Ain't t-t-tellin' tales,
but there's a m-m-monster in them bales."

Scurry, sent to investigate
said, "Somethin's there, make no mistake."
When Monty then came into sight
Woofbot growled and Panic took flight.

The 'monster' spoke, restoring calm
and won them over with his charm
They gathered round to make amends
and in no time were best of friends.

THE STING

Over Hod Hill and close to White Mill
Scratchy Bottom Farm had an auction
And Major Payne went to the event
with cheque book, his wallet and caution.

For something to do, Woofbot went too
very glad that he had tagged along
Major Payne knew what he had to do:
buy a tractor – now what could go wrong?

In the marquee, the Major drank tea
and caught the attention of Wally
He felt annoyed – had tried to avoid
'that man' and his flea-bitten collie.

Wally you see, called out – "Anthony!"
which Major Payne found disrespectful
(This man, by golly, built 'Rooster's Folly'
which was, indeed, more than regretful!).

"Horses," said Wally, "go with your Folly.
Cheap tractor, though, could be a curse."
The Major stood proud, told him aloud,
"Buy a horse? I would eat my hat first!"

On Major Payne's mind – still had to find
a tractor that would meet all his needs.
Found 'Lot 59', thought it looked fine
and would see what the bidding achieved.

Some time round noon, in the auction room
Major Payne wiped his brow with a cloth
The jacket he'd got made him too hot
so removed it and then nodded off.

On 'Lot 64', in through the door
came a wasp which went 'buzzzz' round his head
Hand flailed high, caught the auctioneer's eye,
he'd been stung and the wasp was now dead!

Feeling a twit – was loathe to admit
he knew not what he'd won with his bid
And though that was so, he would soon know
that a one certain somebody did!

Clip clop, clip clop – the Major's face dropped,
dreading what he knew would follow
Hand to his head, "Ant," Wally said,
"Bet that was a hard hat to swallow!"

SHELL SHOCKED!

The Major was so excited
that his face shone with a smile
'cos JO3LL – the jeep that he'd restored
was ready for him to trial.

He'd waited long and patiently
for this very day to come
But with the pride now felt inside
were butterflies in his tum.

Woofbot aboard, he turned the key
(at the map took one last peep)
then foot on gas, clutch in, brake off
they were on their way – BEEP! BEEP!

The air was fresh, they'd not a care
as they cruised along the lanes
Until, low flying overhead
with a loud BOOOOOM! came a plane.

JO3LL kangarooed along the road,
metal began to rattle
Much like it had done in the war
when bombed by planes in battle.

The engine stalled, the Major cussed
but fixed it with a spanner
Though, he was much more in the mood
to bash it with a hammer.

The day was bad, but got much worse
when JO3LL with faulty wiring
was spooked by blasts on 'Army Range'
where guns and tanks were firing.

As man and beast now held their breath
and the jeep turned tail to zoom
when brakes then failed and all seemed lost
they were forced to face their doom!

Now racing home with shaking bones
(poor Woofbot feeling queazy)
the Major sweat, his shirt was wet
and pants were somewhat 'breezy!'

A sudden stop – JO3LL on his nose
had the Major truly flung
Up, up he went, 'til bum was dumped
on a pile of smelly dung!

MONEY FOR METAL

Dimple was ablaze with colour
much bunting was draped in the square
and in the streets were rows of stalls
with local folk selling their wares.

Woofbot went off with the Mayor
(which may have started the rumours)
and Major Payne went down the street
stopping outside 'Bessie's Bloomers.'

Her shop brought a smile to his face,
eyes feasting on tarts he could see
Such treats were a tasty delight
Doc. Duttock, though, would not agree.

He'd told the Major to diet
and warned him – that if he dare cheat
the bloomer bread, cakes, pies and tarts
would stop him from seeing his feet!

He bought a pair of large blooomers
(the man in front had the last tart)
Bessie then bagged him two cup cakes:
tomorrow the diet would start.

As he left, bumped into Joe King
(a local comedy actor)
then eye spied an ad on the wall
offering 'Bargain buy' tractors.

The Major scribbled the details
(there were few cheap tractors about)
then driving off in his 'Bubble'
decided to go check it out.

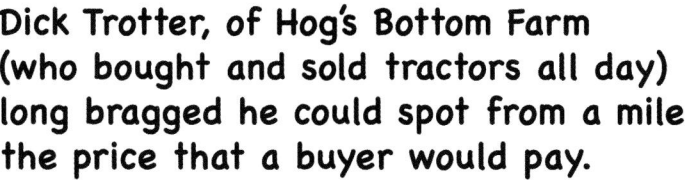

Dick Trotter, of Hog's Bottom Farm
(who bought and sold tractors all day)
long bragged he could spot from a mile
the price that a buyer would pay.

Dick's 'facts' were so lacking in truth,
he was not a man you could trust
and tractors that had many faults
were painted to cover up rust.

The Major soon knew he'd been duped
(much like he was with the Folly)
And ripping him off for repairs,
Dick must have thought – what a wally!

TWO HOOTS

Olive, tethered to a perch,
head under wing, was scheming
To her owner all seemed well:
his little owl was preening.

She had in mind – a fowl plan
to escape from cross-eyed Coots
Win freedom from the cruel hand
of a man not worth two hoots!

Olive dreamt of adventure
and the freedom of the air
Loathed those captive bird displays
for a crowd that did not care.

Then, one afternoon...

A storm broke without warning
and fat Coots, out in the rain
chased by a dog, fell in a bog
never to be seen again.

Crowds dispersed, lightning flashed
and the clouds, now fit to burst
sped across an angry sky
as the tempest did its worst!

Porky Pete, with stinky feet,
then released the birds of prey
His livelihood gone for good
when they upped and flew away.

Eagles, falcons, Olive too
(whom by the four winds were blown)
cared not a jot – Coots was gone
and the skies were theirs to roam.

Happy Bottom felt the storm
(the barn roof had been damaged)
Buckets were placed on the floor
so all leaks could be managed.

Olive sheltered in the barn
for this was where wind brought her
Sleepy though, she fell from beam
and... *Sploshed!*
into some water!

Woofbot gently scooped her out
with help from Fireside too
She wiped her beak – tried to speak
but was now too wet – to woo!

METAL MENACE!

CRASH! BANG! WALLOP!

Ploughing into a stack of bales
this clumsy metal 'creature'
to those now fearing loss of limb
had no redeeming feature.

As mayhem spread and 'cheeps' then fled
Napoleon - not amused
demand that 'it' apologise
but was, point blank, refused.

Hettie was in a fowl temper
TJ couldn't give tuppence
but Woofbot said, "Don't egg him on
'cos he'll get his comeuppance!"

'MURDER' ON THE LAWN

The barn was no place for a cat
that would not kill a mouse or rat
to Fireside this would be a sin
'cos food for cats comes in a tin.

All curled up, licking her paw,
two noses poked up through the straw
Panic and Scurry were two friends
on whom she knew she could depend.

"Things aren't as bad as they 'ave been,"
said Scurry, as Olive from a beam
flew down to join the 'merry' band
to see if she could lend a 'hand'.

"Panic," said Scurry, "we must die.
Now listen up 'cos this is why.
If Fireside was a rodent ripper
her reward would be a kipper."

Panic squealed, "That would be murder!"
(man on the moon must have heard her)
Scurry then whispered to her ear
"Trust in me. You've nothing to fear."

After Scurry'd explained the spoof
Olive was stationed on the roof
The stage was set and she did well
to jab a twig against the bell.

      DING!
        DONG!

The Major, standing at his door
witnessed a sight not seen before
Fireside caught mice, then, as he'd said,
on the lawn – she killed them dead!

Olive then caught the Major's eye
(which was the plan) as she flew by
the mice were gone, Fireside looked smug
but as she curled up on her rug...

"I've let you in," the Major said,
"but as you've on two mice just fed,
you'll get no fish and that is that,
'til you show me you've killed a rat!"

BUZZZzz..!

The Major snuffled in his bed
as daring fly buzzed round his head
When nose was tickled, he then sneezed
and sprayed the fly, who was snot pleased.

Now out of bed, not feeling bright
(can't say he looked a pretty sight)
he swiped the air – began to prance
the fly amused to watch him 'dance'.

The fly scoffed when the Major said,
"Buzz off, before I splat you dead!"
With room now wrecked, he cursed the pest
but left the mess, whilst getting dressed.

Down in the kitchen, made a drink,
then standing propped beside the sink
that kamikaze fly buzzed up
and...
    PLOPPED
       into his coffee cup!

"I've gotcha now!" the Major cried.
It couldn't swim, although it tried
He flicked it out, but failed to splat
so fly buzzed off – oh darn and drat!

After lunch, beginning to tire,
the Major napped beside the fire
and would have been extremely vexed
if he'd known what would happen next...

The fly back round the Major's head
chose to ignore what he had said
But when he next sucked air to snore
both got more than they bargained for...

GULP!

HUMBLED

Spring had sprung and the day was bright
but this busiest time for most
was soon to become disrupted
by a tractor too keen to boast.

TJ'd been out on a 'mission'
and now safely back from the coast,
said clearing the seaweed from sand
was what he liked doing the most.

His talk of fun and adventure,
a mile or two from Durdle Door
had Monty trying to picture
a place he would love to explore.

The next day, the Major went out
so Monty, now up to no good
said, "TJ let's go to the beach."
But he wasn't sure that they should.

"It would be bonkers," said Winnie
"You two may well drown in the sea."
"Drowning's for nags, " TJ replied,
"Not mega machines such as me."

"Watch what you're saying," warned Winston
"We're older and wiser than you.
One day you may well eat your words
and need us before we need you."

"You're old and useless," said TJ
"And I'm now willing to wager
that you two will see flying pigs
before doing me a favour."

TJ took up Monty's challenge,
unaware what the dangers could be
And whilst they had fun on the sand
they kept a blind eye to the sea.

Waves came crashing in from afar
and the tide was rising higher
When TJ revved, his engine stalled
and wheels got stuck in the mire.

Monty, marooned on the tractor,
was swept by a wave to the beach
and would have tried to help his friend
but he was now beyond his reach.

Driving along the old cliff road,
came the Major in his 'Bubble'
He stopped, binoculars in hand
having spied something in trouble.

He looked and looked, then said aloud,
"Cor blimey! This cannot be true!"
With tractor drowning in the sea
what was the poor Major to do?

Long owed a favour from a mate
he borrowed a livestock trailer
But horses now on sandy shore
had a mind to win a wager.

Winston and Winnie stood their ground
(as the Major's face contorted)
He coaxed and cussed, told them to – "PULL!"
But they shook their heads and snorted.

The waves reared high, the hour was nigh
and with TJ's life now fated
Winston and Winnie eyed the sky
as they played for time and waited...

Then...

Winnie looking at Winston said
(the Major now dancing a jig)
"This 'mean machine' will surely die
if we wait for the flying pigs."

Monty came home with the Major
of sea salt and seaweed he reeked
TJ, though, got his comeuppance
and ate 'humble pie' for a week!

The theft, or seaside mystery
was a case that was never solved
which came as no surprise, of course,
to all those who had been involved!

FLUSHED!

Major Payne on the loo had to stand

whilst he painted his ceiling by hand

In tin, brush was dipped

but when his foot slipped

the result was not quite what he'd planned!

TICK TOCK...

One night, as stars were shining bright,
the barn, now bathed in pale moonlight
kept horses, cat, mice, owl and more
all safe and snug behind its doors.

But then, amid the farts and snores
a silent 'shadow' snuck through straw
As startled Panic squealed with fright
her eyes went wide and chest grew tight.

She'd seen the past – that place they'd fled,
woke poor Scurry, to whom she said,
"Black Eye's coming. Can feel his power.
He's getting closer, hour by hour!"

"You've had a nightmare," Scurry said.
"This fear is all inside your head.
We're safe 'ere and not movin' on.
Now go to sleep: the past is gone …"

PIDDLE PANIC!

History repeats – JO3LL was downbeat
(hadn't wanted to cause any harm)
Now left to rot, what hope had he got
of enjoying a life on the farm?

Feared this was the end – but he had friends
and though he had caused them to panic
For him they felt sad – did not think bad
'cos JO3LL was more 'shell shocked' than manic!

"Pssst!" came a call from a wall made of straw
It was Scurry, with something to spout
Told JO3LL he cared, that his pain was shared
by the friends who would soon get him out.

JO3LL was confused and asked what they'd use
to enable their scheme to succeed
Scurry didn't know – said he would go
and collect all the things they might need.

The day Major Payne set off for Spain
the carnival swung into Dimple
Monty, to those who wanted to go,
said he'd hatch a plan, plain and simple.

It was thought wise – that JO3LL be disguised
planning for which was meticulous
But Panic said, "No! I will not go.
You're mad. The scheme is ridiculous!"

Now each had a task and when at last
they stood to admire their contraption
Monty aloud, said they should feel proud
their float was now ready for action!

With Major Payne gone – game was now on
and as Monty swung open the doors,
everyone gawked – their eyes were on stalks
and the air was soon filled with applause.

On country roads (which still had those toads)
went their 'carnival float' at a trot
Arriving in town, sun shining down,
were amazed by the greeting they got.

Procession with bands, flag waving hands,
no merrier a sight could there be
But over too soon, mid afternoon
they followed the crowds to the quay.

Scurry and more, went off to explore
and the horses strolled off to eat grass
Monty, meanwhile, sat there in style,
put a smile on the faces that passed.

Later that day, Red Arrows Display
came overhead roaring like thunder
JO3LL came alive and took as he dived,
poor Monty, whom Piddle would plunder.

A commotion was heard, but more absurd
was the Mayor falling off the pontoon
Folk ran about, could not get him out
and his rescue could not come too soon.

Young Jim Flappers ran like the clappers
to collect an inflatable whale
It floated a while, then farted in style
when its tail got impaled on a nail!

Casting a rope, gave Mayor false hope
but at least some could say they had tried
When rescue fell through, launched a canoe
but in no time at all it capsized!

Next, on a whim, Flash Harry jumped in
his prank, though, was not reassuring
But further downstream, Woofbot had seen
a 'thing' in the Piddle was stirring.

Out from the deep, amphibious jeep
then provided the crowd with a thrill
Sat there inside, enjoying the ride –
was the Mayor with a hand on the wheel!